LETTING GO
OF ED -
EMBRACING ME

A JOURNAL OF SELF-DISCOVERY

Published in Australia by
LMD Publishing
Melbourne Australia

Email: info@apttherapeuticsolutions.com
Website: www.APTTherapeuticsolutions.com

First published in Australia 2019
Copyright © Maria Ganci & Lindsey Atkins 2019

NATIONAL
LIBRARY
OF AUSTRALIA

National Library of Australia Cataloguing –in – Publication entry
Ganci Maria, Atkins Linsey, authors
Letting go of Ed, Embracing Me – A Journal of Self-Discovery
ISBN: 978-0-9944746-4-3 (paperback)
ISBN: 978-0-9944746-5-0 (epub)

Printed by Kindle Direct Publishing

Disclaimer

THIS JOURNAL OF DISCOVERY

BELONGS TO

....

IT IS MY PERSONAL

STRENGTHS & MY DETERMINATION

THAT WILL GUIDE ME

TO MY DESTINATION

OF LOVE, COMPASSION, & ACCEPTANCE

OF MY TRUE SELF

PURPOSE & USE OF THIS JOURNAL

Adolescence can be a difficult and confusing time, but it is also a time of self-discovery. During adolescence, you think more seriously about the person you want to be and the values you want to live by. It also marks the beginning of establishing your own personal identity. You are a unique human being and there is, and never will be, another you. Your adolescent journey is also the time when you develop important skills that enable you to realize your full potential and, ultimately, create a sense of meaning and purpose for your life in preparation for adulthood.

Unfortunately, an eating disorder can derail the wonderful development that happens during adolescence. The critical voice in your head makes you feel worthless. It negates your strengths. It denies your potential. It tricks you into believing that you are totally in control of everything and that the more perfect you are, the more in control you are.

This over-control even extends to what you eat and how you look. Over time, these beliefs become strong neural pathways in your brain. They become so entrenched that you start to believe this is the only way to live and to succeed in life, and the result is a vicious cycle of negative reinforcement. The more you believe this, the more your brain accepts what you believe, and your beliefs then create your reality.

The truth is, however, that you are totally out of control. The sense of control you believe you have is driven by the anxiety and fear of losing control reinforced by an ever present inner critical voice. Unfortunately, many adolescents believe they are powerless to change anything or there is no escape.

So how can we help you get out of these neural trenches? The only way out of this situation is to rewire your brain and replace the negative neural pathways with new realistic pathways that allow you to stand up to your harsh inner critic and discover and accept your true, beautiful self. Only then can you realize your true potential.

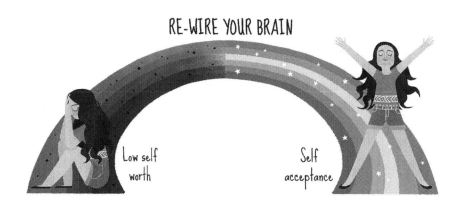

This journal shows you how to do this by taking advantage of the brain's neuroplasticity. Neuroplasticity is a natural process in your brain and refers to its ability to change and adapt to changes in your environment. It will adapt much quicker if you consciously direct your brain to change. However, new pathways don't develop overnight. Rewiring the brain requires certain conditions, including:

- Focused attention on what you want to change – This strengthens synaptic connections.

- Repetition and practice – This develops the new pathways more quickly. Practice can be done in your imagination as well.

- Motivation – You need to really want the new behavior you are focusing on.

- Novelty (learning) and pleasure – Learning new things stimulates the brain, and deriving satisfaction from the activity releases dopamine, a powerful chemical in your body that reinforces the behavior with positive feelings. Novelty and pleasure also create emotional arousal, which connects the feeling (limbic) brain with the thinking (cortical) brain, helping you focus and enjoy repetition.

Our brain is a product of our distant ancestors and is predisposed toward negativity and sensing danger in order to keep us safe. However, over-activation in this area can lead to excessive anticipatory anxiety, which is not a good long-term psychological outcome. To help you overcome your anxiety and fear, this journal aims to help you step outside your comfort zone and view fear as an opportunity for growth.

The comfort zone is a well-established psychological term that describes the mental and physical space you feel safe and comfortable in. Your comfort zone provides familiarity, predictability, and consistency and is usually a place where you feel free of anxiety and fear. The downside of constantly staying within your comfort zone is that you will miss many opportunities to grow psychologically and you also risk not attaining your full potential. Growth is only achieved by taking the risk of stepping outside your comfort zone.

> "Your comfort zone is a beautiful place,
> but nothing ever grows there"
>
> (Author unknown)

Your brain is a goal-directed machine and benefits from having a target to focus on. Before you embark on your journey, we suggest that you set several personal goals you wish to achieve in the next six months. They do not need to be major goals but several things you would like to change in your life.

Your goals should also be linked to your personal values. Alternatively, your goal can be a value that you would like to further develop. A value is a standard that you believe in and want to live by. Make sure your value is not influenced by societal or peer values; otherwise, you are just conforming to other people's standards and you are not being true to yourself. As you reflect daily on your goals, your brain will subconsciously guide you toward your goal as you allow it to enter your awareness on a regular basis.

This journal provides a simple yet powerful guide to help you rewire your brain on your journey of self-discovery. The questions contained in the journal are scientifically based and focused on developing self-compassion, mindfulness, gratitude, and a sense of purpose in your life. Additionally, the journal will help you develop emotional self-awareness, help you feel connected to others, help you discover and live your values, and develop positivity and appreciation of your strengths. You can also use this journal to reflect on life events and tasks and break them down into small, manageable chunks of time and meaning. The exercises are all geared toward learning new ways of thinking and feeling that will ultimately rewire your brain.

It is important to remember that the time you devote to your journal should not feel demanding, or it will just become a chore lacking stimulation and will inhibit change. The aim is that journaling becomes a healthy and enjoyable self-reflective habit that can help you calm your thoughts and emotions. As you progress along your journey, journaling will become an enjoyable habit and you will develop your own preferred style of journaling. It is important that you write what you feel as well as give yourself permission to express what you feel without guilt.

There are several appendices attached with helpful suggestions if you get stuck, as many adolescents initially find self-reflection a little difficult. Appendix A is a list of values to help you think about what you value. Appendix B provides a diagram to help you explore emotions. Finally, Appendix C is a list of affirmations that you can draw from if you need guidance, but we encourage you to develop your own.

QUALITIES THAT THE JOURNAL AIMS TO DEVELOP

SELF-COMPASSION

Self-compassion is a wonderful personal attribute to develop. Self-compassion is basically being kind to yourself and accepting yourself and your mistakes. Research shows that practicing self-compassion and being kinder to yourself improves your mental health and reduces depression, stress, and anxiety. Research also shows that **most people** treat their friends more compassionately than they treat themselves.

There are probably many moments throughout the day when you have felt compassion or practiced compassion for others without any conscious awareness. In general, adolescents are very caring of their friends and quickly provide emotional and physical support. However, most adolescents would never say the critical things that they say to themselves to their friends. Become aware of these moments and think about why you treat yourself so harshly. Compassion also leads to a sense of connection with humanity because if you treat yourself with kindness, so you will treat others.

Each day, make a conscious effort to have at least one self-compassionate thought, affirmation, or self-caring action. Reflecting on and writing these self-compassionate acts in your journal will help you develop a mindful approach toward yourself, others, and the environment.

GRATITUDE

Gratitude is a powerful connecting emotion. Regular expressions of gratitude deepen our connection to and compassion for others and our environment. Sometimes it's difficult to feel grateful or appreciative, especially when you are suffering;  when you feel down; or when you feel things are not going the way you would like them to go.

At such times, it is much easier to focus on the negative aspects of your life and forget all the positive things. This can leave you caught in a downward spiral of negativity. Because of this, it is important to take a few moments each day to notice the small and meaningful things in your life. This can include the people who love and support you; the beautiful and soothing things in your environment and in nature, such as the warmth of the sun or perfume of a flower; and all the wonderful opportunities you have been given.

Try to acknowledge the great things about yourself even if you currently don't believe you have any. By expressing gratitude in your journal each day, you will quickly feel a greater connection to everyone and everything and reduce any feelings of isolation. Scientific research has repeatedly proven that acts of gratitude and expressing thanks are extremely beneficial to our health and well-being. Remember, a little gratitude goes a long way.

CONNECTEDNESS

Human beings are social creatures, and from the moment we are born, our survival depends on being connected and understood by others. Psychological  research tells us time and time again that the most important factor in leading a happy and healthy life is a positive sense of connection to others.

During adolescence, connection is especially important because it is through our connection with our friends, school, and family that we can develop a sense of who we are. Many mental health problems stem from a sense of loneliness and alienation from others, which displaces our sense of connection. When we feel others don't accept us, we struggle to accept ourselves. Likewise, when we don't accept ourselves, others also struggle to accept us. This can leave us feeling stuck in a vicious cycle of feeling ineffective and worthless. But remember, connection is an individual responsibility, and many make the mistake of waiting for others to reach out and connect with us.

Make it a practice every day to take one small action to connect with others either by word or action. Perhaps you could make a connection with two or three people each day by smiling at them, asking how they are, or making a positive comment you think they would enjoy. For example, you could say, "Gee, Jayne, I really like the way you did that" or "Thomas, it's really great having you around." Write them in your journal and reflect on how these small acts of kindness made you and the other person feel. Try to step out of your comfort zone and connect with people you don't know very well.

While connecting to others is important, self-connection is just as critical. Connecting to yourself encompasses connecting to your body, your emotions, your creativity, and your values. Connecting to yourself is striving to learn more about yourself and how you function and is one of the main aims of this journal.

Equally important is connecting with nature. The benefits of being in natural surroundings have been extensively researched. We encourage you to try to make a habit of connecting with nature every day even if it is just taking a deep breath of fresh air outside, pondering a beautiful flower or tree, or looking at the stars for a few minutes.

AFFIRMATIONS

Affirmations are positive statements about who you want to be, how you want to live your life, and what you want to achieve. Most importantly, affirmations are powerful statements that can reprogram your thought patterns and change the way you think and  feel about things. Bruce Lee, the world-renowned martial artist said, "As you think, so shall you become."

Affirmations should always be stated in the present tense as if you already possess the desired trait and start with the words "I am," followed by the desired attribute. "I am" are two of the most powerful words that can be said, and whatever follows "I am" you invite into your life and it commences the creation of your desire. Affirmations also need to be stated with intention and belief. They have much more power if said aloud and written down. Don't rely on validation from others to create your self-worth. Self-worth is created internally from your own beliefs. "I am" statements will transform your life, as your internal thoughts create your external reality.

MINDFULNESS

Mindfulness is bringing one's attention to the present moment without judgment. Mindfulness alleviates stress, improves emotion regulation, and creates greater clarity of mind. The questions in this journal aim to help increase your awareness of what is going on around you and happening to you throughout your day. We also want you to develop an awareness of how you respond to situations via your thoughts, senses, and emotions. Understanding your response style can help you manage under and over reactions to certain situations.

As you answer the questions, think about how you felt physically and emotionally. Become aware of the feeling in your body. More importantly, reflect on how you feel while writing about the experience. As you become more mindfully aware, your ability to self-regulate will steadily increase. Mindfulness is not meditation but the practice of developing a full awareness of yourself and surroundings in the present moment.

A simple exercise in mindfulness can be done in your classroom. As you enter your classroom, stop for several seconds and become aware of the room and who is in the room. Notice your thoughts and any sensations in your body. Do you feel alert or tired and distracted?

You can also access free mindful exercises at **www.apttherapeuticsolutions.com**.

EMOTIONAL AWARENESS

Emotions are our non-verbal language. It is the language we used from birth and the language that continues to develop even after we learn how to speak. Did you know that over 80% of our communication is non-verbal and that humans rely on emotional language more than any other method to communicate? Emotions help us interpret our environment; they let others know how we feel and what we need; and they help us interpret and respond to the needs of others. If we see someone sad or crying, we are moved emotionally to help them.

Unfortunately, our 'modern' society is becoming less and less open about emotions despite their importance. Cognitive prowess and scientific proof seem to be today's values, yet our intrinsic self is based on emotions. Emotions are protective, but when they become overwhelming, they can also become destructive. It is important to be aware of your emotions and the messages they are trying to give you.

Some adolescents find it easier to be cut off from their emotions to avoid emotional pain. However, this is not a good idea, as emotions are automatic. Cutting yourself off from your emotions does not make them go away, as you are only suppressing them temporarily. They will eventually emerge in some other way. Each day, take some time to reflect on how you felt emotionally during the day and learn to name and listen to your emotions. Understanding your emotions will give you greater insight into how you can better cope with the demands of being an adolescent.

THE MORNING COMPONENT OF THE JOURNAL

Upon waking we suggest that you spend several minutes doing the following in your journal:

1. Write an affirmation about yourself for the day. Try to repeat it throughout the day, as repetition makes it more powerful. It will remain in your subconscious even after you have stopped thinking about it.

2. Think of one small thing that you can complete today that will take you a step you closer to your goal.

Then close your journal and leave it next to your bed until the evening or before you are ready to go to sleep.

THE EVENING COMPONENT OF THE JOURNAL

The evening component has questions that you can quickly answer to help you reflect on yourself in a mindful way. You should devote at least 5–10 minutes to this activity each evening.

We also encourage you to express yourself on the *"Today's Reflections"* page however you wish. You can write, doodle, paint, draw, and paste photos or pictures. Remember this is meant to be fun and help you become more self-aware. So let your creativity roam free! The journal is private, and it's your choice to share with others or not.

DEVELOP THE HABIT OF JOURNALING

To be effective, journaling must be done on a regular basis. Habits are born out of repetition, and it takes a while to establish a habit – up to 30 or more days. So, it's best to stick to a daily routine for at least that amount of time and then evaluate if journaling is for you and if you found the process beneficial and enjoyable. If you didn't enjoy the process, you can discard it, knowing that you gave it your best shot. Remember, you will never know if you don't have a go!

MY GOALS FOR THE NEXT 6 MONTHS

It's important to set goals for yourself, as they provide direction and a sense of purpose in your life. Having a sense of purpose gives you meaning, which involves believing that your life: a) is significant and worthwhile; b) makes sense; and c) has a purpose. Meaning and purpose drives your internal motivation and is usually enhanced if fuelled by values you are passionate about. Research shows that there is a strong link between a sense of purpose and improved health and wellbeing. Without a sense of purpose, life has little meaning and can lead to boredom and a sense of alienation.

Please take the time to think about your goals and use the boxes below to practice. Make sure you also think about what you value about the goal you have chosen. It does not need to be a major goal and can be small goals toward a larger goal or dream. The exercise is to help you focus on what you value and what you would like to achieve in your life. You can have several goals—personal, social, or academic.

MY GOAL

VALUE RELATED TO GOAL

MEDIUM STEPS TOWARD GOAL

SMALL STEPS TOWARD GOAL

FEAR VS. COURAGE

Before you commence on your journey of self-discovery, we briefly want to introduce you to the emotion "fear" and learn to see fear as a friend and not as a foe.

FEAR is one of our primary emotions, and its role is to keep us safe. Without fear, we would continually expose ourselves to, or remain in, dangerous situations and probably wouldn't survive for very long. This is the healthy aspect of fear because it has a protective role. However, when fear predominantly makes you see and experience the world as a threatening place, it becomes a destructive emotion that continually increases your anxiety.

Fear underlies and drives many of our interactions and behaviors. Despite some people displaying a 'brave front,' everyone experiences fear. There are diverse fears, and everyone has their own unique fears, just as everyone differs in their capacity to manage their fear. The most common fears that adolescents experience include:

Fear of rejection; Fear of losing control over aspects of their lives;

Fear of failure; and Fear of not being good enough.

Fear can be a crippling emotion that destroys your sense of self and creates a barrier between you and achieving your potential. Fear keeps you trapped within the walls of your comfort zone. Fear won't allow you to take risks; it won't allow you to grow psychologically; and it sabotages your dreams. Fear becomes the obstacle between you and your potential. Your potential lies behind your wall of fear, and you need to cross that barrier if you are to realize your potential.

One frustrating thing is that our brain can easily create fear when none exists. This happens when the thinking brain starts to imagine and ruminate about all the things that can go wrong, which then triggers an automatic hormonal 'fight or flight' response to a danger that was just imagined. Sometimes the brain is not good at discriminating between real and imagined danger because it can be directed by strong threatening thoughts, which generate real anxiety and fear in the limbic system. Your brain's ability to create fears from nothing is important to remember when learning to deal with anxiety.

It may be difficult to accept that fear is a story you have constructed in your own mind. The more you believe in your fear, the more powerful and bigger it gets and can easily become overwhelming. As a result, it is sometimes easier to stay inside your comfort zone where you feel safe. It is also important to remember that whatever you allow your brain to mentally create becomes your physical reality.

The constructive side of fear is that you can see fear as a supportive friend or teacher who is providing you with the opportunity to grow stronger. Every time you feel fearful, instead of seeing it as an  obstacle in your life, think of it as an opportunity to grow. Every time you do something you are fearful of doing or believe you can't do, you grow emotionally and psychologically. As you overcome your fear, your confidence grows; you feel satisfied with yourself; and you are happier within yourself. Every time you face your fear, it is a step closer to realizing your potential. Try to develop your own mantra, such as, "Fear is the seed of growth."

COURAGE is the emotion that can stand up to fear.

The best way to combat your fear is to confront it with courage. Just think of the movies you have watched where the plot centers on a battle of good versus evil. Well, your brain is dealing with a similar scenario day after day, but it is a battle of fear versus courage. Just like the movies, it's always good to have that happy ending where good triumphs over evil, and it's your compassionate self that always wants courage to outsmart fear.

To overcome your fear, you first need to become aware and acknowledge your fear, name the fear, and then learn to stand up to the fear by taking small and consistent steps toward your fear. Reflect on your internal battle. What are you battling, why has it become a battle, and what keeps you stuck in the battle?

Read the following fable about the Wolf of Courage and the Wolf of Fear. The concept has helped hundreds of adolescents understand their internal battles with fear and anxiety. Hopefully, the fable will help you realize that you also possess courage within yourself to stand up to fear.

Again reflect on your internal battle and think about which wolf you mostly feed. Is it the wolf of fear? Take some time each day to visualize yourself feeding your wolf of courage. Help your wolf of courage to grow strong and stand up to the wolf of fear.

Feeding your wolf of courage also requires you to step outside your comfort zone even though it may feel confronting and overwhelming. Make a daily habit of taking one small step outside your comfort zone and write about it in your journal so you have confirmation of your achievements.

THE WOLF OF COURAGE AND THE WOLF OF FEAR

Story by Greg Amundson –
The Warrior & The Monk: A Fable about Fulfilling your
Potential and Finding True Happiness

*Many thanks to Greg Amundson for permission to use his work
to support young people in reaching their potential.*

Many years ago, a wise monk spoke to a young boy the evening before he would begin the ritual inauguration into the warrior tradition. The young boy was apprehensive and uncertain of his ability to succeed in the harsh training and conditions that would follow. The wise monk told the young boy,

"There are two wolves engaged in a fierce battle within your mind:

A Wolf of Courage

And

A Wolf of Fear."

The young boy asked the old sage, "Which wolf will be victorious in the battle?"

"Whichever wolf you feed," the wise monk replied.

"In that case," the young boy thought aloud, "I must feed the Wolf of Courage."

"The Wolf of Courage and the Wolf of Fear are both starving for your attention, which is governed by your thoughts and words. A warrior must have discipline and willpower to think and speak positively.

Only positive thoughts and words shall feed the Wolf of Courage."

Hearing this ancient story retold by the wise monk elated the young warrior and captured his imagination. The story also sparked his interest in the power of not only thoughts but of words as well.

"Wise monk, in the story, you said the Wolf of Courage was fed by both thoughts and words. What effect does my speaking have in the world of effects?"

The wise monk replied,

"Your speaking is the first effect of your thinking. Every word you speak creates a ripple throughout the entire Universe.

Your speaking influences your actions, and over time and with repetition, your actions shape the person you become."

With a startled expression on his face, the young warrior exclaimed, "I had no idea my thoughts and words were so powerful!"

"Indeed, young warrior," the wise monk said, "they are the seeds you plant in the fertile soil of pure potentiality."

To help the young warrior understand the magnitude of the power his thoughts and words contained, the wise monk continued,

"A farmer who plants an apple seed is not surprised when an apple tree begins to grow, for the apple seed produced after its own kind. In the same manner, your words produce like seeds. Everything you say takes on life, and in time, everything you say will be returned to you in some way, shape, or form."

Hearing this, the young warrior asked, "Is this why I must discipline my thinking?"

The wise monk said with encouragement,

"Yes, that is correct. Your thinking is the point of inception for everything you speak. Therefore, by disciplining your thinking, you begin to speak the language of positive expectancy." The wise monk then gently put his hands on the young warrior's shoulders, and said, "Remember this sequence of events, and you can assure yourself a future of Prosperity, Love, and Fulfilment…

**Positive thoughts
lead to positive words,
which produce after their kind, resulting
in positive experiences
within every area of your life."**

DATE_____

MORNING REFLECTION

My affirmation for today:

_____

_____

One step I will take today that allows me to leave my comfort zone and leads me closer to my goal:

_____

_____

_____

_____

EVENING REFLECTION

One thing that I am grateful for today and why I am grateful:

_____

_____

_____

_____

A thing I enjoyed today: _____

_____

_____

A person who inspired me today and why they inspired me:_____

_____

_____

_____

_____

My act of connection to others today:_____

_____

_____

_____

_____

A value I lived by today:_____

_____

_____

_____

An emotion I felt today _____ and what

was my emotion trying to tell me?_____

_____

_____

_____

_____

An act of self-compassion today: _____

_____

_____

_____

_____

Did I leave my comfort zone today and do something to bring me closer to my goal?_____

_____

_____

_____

_____

Which wolf did I feed today? _____

_____

_____

_____

_____

SELF-REFLECTIONS

Use this page to explore your thoughts and feelings
and relationship with ED.

_____

_____

_____

_____

_____

_____

_____

_____

_____

_____

_____

_____

_____

_____

_____

_____

_____

_____

BLANK PAGE FOR DRAWING, PASTING, MAPPING, & EXPLORING

you are
strong

DATE_____

MORNING REFLECTION

My affirmation for today:

_____

_____

One step I will take today that allows me to leave my comfort zone and
leads me closer to my goal:

_____

_____

_____

_____

EVENING REFLECTION

One thing that I am grateful for today and why I am
grateful:

_____

_____

_____

_____

A thing I enjoyed today: _____

_____

_____

A person who inspired me today and why they inspired me:_____

_____

_____

_____

_____

My act of connection to others today:_____

_____

_____

_____

_____

A value I lived by today:_____

_____

_____

_____

An emotion I felt today _____ and what

was my emotion trying to tell me?_____

_____

_____

_____

_____

An act of self-compassion today: _____

_____

_____

_____

_____

Did I leave my comfort zone today and do something to bring me

closer to my goal?_____

_____

_____

_____

_____

Which wolf did I feed today? _____

_____

_____

_____

_____

SELF-REFLECTIONS

Use this page to explore your thoughts and feelings
and relationship with ED.

_____

_____

_____

_____

_____

_____

_____

_____

_____

_____

_____

_____

_____

_____

_____

_____

_____

BLANK PAGE FOR DRAWING, PASTING, MAPPING, & EXPLORING

I AM PERFECTLY IMPERFECT

DATE_____

MORNING REFLECTION

My affirmation for today:

_____

_____

One step I will take today that allows me to leave my comfort zone and leads me closer to my goal:

_____

_____

_____

_____

EVENING REFLECTION

One thing that I am grateful for today and why I am grateful:

_____

_____

_____

_____

A thing I enjoyed today: _____

_____

_____

A person who inspired me today and why they inspired me:_____

_____

_____

_____

_____

My act of connection to others today:_____

_____

_____

_____

_____

A value I lived by today:_____

_____

_____

_____

An emotion I felt today _____ and what

was my emotion trying to tell me?_____

_____

_____

_____

_____

An act of self-compassion today: _____

_____

_____

_____

_____

Did I leave my comfort zone today and do something to bring me

closer to my goal?_____

_____

_____

_____

_____

Which wolf did I feed today? _____

_____

_____

_____

_____

SELF-REFLECTIONS

Use this page to explore your thoughts and feelings
and relationship with ED.

_____

_____

_____

_____

_____

_____

_____

_____

_____

_____

_____

_____

_____

_____

_____

_____

BLANK PAGE FOR DRAWING, PASTING, MAPPING, & EXPLORING

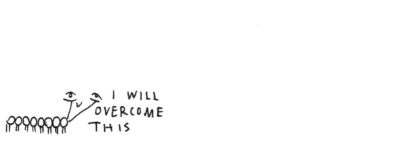

DATE_____

Morning Reflection

My affirmation for today:

_____

_____

One step I will take today that allows me to leave my comfort zone and leads me closer to my goal:

_____

_____

_____

_____

Evening Reflection

One thing that I am grateful for today and why I am grateful:

_____

_____

_____

_____

A thing I enjoyed today: _____

_____

_____

A person who inspired me today and why they inspired me:_____

_____

_____

_____

_____

My act of connection to others today:_____

_____

_____

_____

_____

A value I lived by today:_____

_____

_____

_____

An emotion I felt today _____ and what

was my emotion trying to tell me?_____

_____

_____

_____

_____

An act of self-compassion today: _____

_____

_____

_____

_____

Did I leave my comfort zone today and do something to bring me

closer to my goal?_____

_____

_____

_____

_____

Which wolf did I feed today? _____

_____

_____

_____

_____

SELF-REFLECTIONS

Use this page to explore your thoughts and feelings
and relationship with ED.

_____

_____

_____

_____

_____

_____

_____

_____

_____

_____

_____

_____

_____

_____

_____

BLANK PAGE FOR DRAWING, PASTING, MAPPING, & EXPLORING

you are
kind

DATE_____

MORNING REFLECTION

My affirmation for today:

_____

_____

One step I will take today that allows me to leave my comfort zone and leads me closer to my goal:

_____

_____

_____

_____

EVENING REFLECTION

One thing that I am grateful for today and why I am grateful:

_____

_____

_____

_____

A thing I enjoyed today: _____

_____

_____

A person who inspired me today and why they inspired me:_____

_____

_____

_____

_____

My act of connection to others today:_____

_____

_____

_____

_____

A value I lived by today:_____

_____

_____

_____

An emotion I felt today _____ and what

was my emotion trying to tell me?_____

_____

_____

_____

_____

An act of self-compassion today: _____

_____

_____

_____

_____

Did I leave my comfort zone today and do something to bring me

closer to my goal?_____

_____

_____

_____

_____

Which wolf did I feed today? _____

_____

_____

_____

_____

SELF-REFLECTIONS

Use this page to explore your thoughts and feelings
and relationship with ED.

_____

_____

_____

_____

_____

_____

_____

_____

_____

_____

_____

_____

_____

_____

_____

_____

_____

BLANK PAGE FOR DRAWING, PASTING, MAPPING, & EXPLORING

DATE_____

MORNING REFLECTION

My affirmation for today:

_____

_____

One step I will take today that allows me to leave my comfort zone and leads me closer to my goal:

_____

_____

_____

_____

EVENING REFLECTION

One thing that I am grateful for today and why I am grateful:

_____

_____

_____

_____

A thing I enjoyed today: _____

_____

_____

A person who inspired me today and why they inspired me:_____

_____

_____

_____

_____

My act of connection to others today:_____

_____

_____

_____

_____

A value I lived by today:_____

_____

_____

_____

An emotion I felt today _____ and what

was my emotion trying to tell me?_____

_____

_____

_____

_____

An act of self-compassion today: _____

_____

_____

_____

_____

Did I leave my comfort zone today and do something to bring me

closer to my goal?_____

_____

_____

_____

_____

Which wolf did I feed today? _____

_____

_____

_____

_____

SELF-REFLECTIONS

Use this page to explore your thoughts and feelings
and relationship with ED.

_____

_____

_____

_____

_____

_____

_____

_____

_____

_____

_____

_____

_____

_____

_____

_____

_____

BLANK PAGE FOR DRAWING, PASTING, MAPPING, & EXPLORING

I don't need to be perfect

DATE_____

Morning Reflection

My affirmation for today:

_____

_____

One step I will take today that allows me to leave my comfort zone and leads me closer to my goal:

_____

_____

_____

_____

Evening Reflection

One thing that I am grateful for today and why I am grateful:

_____

_____

_____

_____

A thing I enjoyed today: _____

_____

_____

A person who inspired me today and why they inspired me:_____

_____

_____

_____

_____

My act of connection to others today:_____

_____

_____

_____

_____

A value I lived by today:_____

_____

_____

_____

An emotion I felt today _____ and what

was my emotion trying to tell me?_____

_____

_____

_____

_____

An act of self-compassion today: _____

_____

_____

_____

_____

Did I leave my comfort zone today and do something to bring me
closer to my goal?_____

_____

_____

_____

_____

Which wolf did I feed today? _____

_____

_____

_____

_____

SELF-REFLECTIONS

Use this page to explore your thoughts and feelings
and relationship with ED.

_____

_____

_____

_____

_____

_____

_____

_____

_____

_____

_____

_____

_____

_____

_____

_____

BLANK PAGE FOR DRAWING, PASTING, MAPPING, & EXPLORING

you are
precious

DATE_____

MORNING REFLECTION

My affirmation for today:

_____

_____

One step I will take today that allows me to leave my comfort zone and leads me closer to my goal:

_____

_____

_____

_____

EVENING REFLECTION

One thing that I am grateful for today and why I am grateful:

_____

_____

_____

_____

A thing I enjoyed today: _____

_____

_____

A person who inspired me today and why they inspired me:_____

_____

_____

_____

_____

My act of connection to others today:_____

_____

_____

_____

_____

A value I lived by today:_____

_____

_____

_____

An emotion I felt today _____ and what

was my emotion trying to tell me?_____

_____

_____

_____

_____

An act of self-compassion today: _____

_____

_____

_____

_____

Did I leave my comfort zone today and do something to bring me closer to my goal?_____

_____

_____

_____

_____

Which wolf did I feed today? _____

_____

_____

_____

_____

SELF-REFLECTIONS

Use this page to explore your thoughts and feelings
and relationship with ED.

_____

_____

_____

_____

_____

_____

_____

_____

_____

_____

_____

_____

_____

_____

_____

_____

_____

_____

BLANK PAGE FOR DRAWING, PASTING, MAPPING, & EXPLORING

It's ok to be me!

DATE_____

MORNING REFLECTION

My affirmation for today:

_____

_____

One step I will take today that allows me to leave my comfort zone and leads me closer to my goal:

_____

_____

_____

_____

EVENING REFLECTION

One thing that I am grateful for today and why I am grateful:

_____

_____

_____

_____

A thing I enjoyed today: _____

_____

_____

A person who inspired me today and why they inspired me:_____

_____

_____

_____

_____

My act of connection to others today:_____

_____

_____

_____

_____

A value I lived by today:_____

_____

_____

_____

An emotion I felt today _____ and what

was my emotion trying to tell me?_____

_____

_____

_____

_____

An act of self-compassion today: _____

_____

_____

_____

_____

Did I leave my comfort zone today and do something to bring me

closer to my goal?_____

_____

_____

_____

_____

Which wolf did I feed today? _____

_____

_____

_____

_____

SELF-REFLECTIONS

Use this page to explore your thoughts and feelings
and relationship with ED.

_____

_____

_____

_____

_____

_____

_____

_____

_____

_____

_____

_____

_____

_____

_____

_____

_____

_____

BLANK PAGE FOR DRAWING, PASTING, MAPPING, & EXPLORING

YOU ARE
STRONG

DATE_____

MORNING REFLECTION

My affirmation for today:

_____

_____

One step I will take today that allows me to leave my comfort zone and leads me closer to my goal:

_____

_____

_____

_____

EVENING REFLECTION

One thing that I am grateful for today and why I am grateful:

_____

_____

_____

_____

A thing I enjoyed today: _____

_____

_____

A person who inspired me today and why they inspired me:_____

_____

_____

_____

_____

My act of connection to others today:_____

_____

_____

_____

A value I lived by today:_____

_____

_____

_____

An emotion I felt today _____ and what

was my emotion trying to tell me?_____

_____

_____

_____

_____

An act of self-compassion today: _____

_____

_____

_____

_____

Did I leave my comfort zone today and do something to bring me
closer to my goal?_____

_____

_____

_____

_____

Which wolf did I feed today? _____

_____

_____

_____

_____

SELF-REFLECTIONS

Use this page to explore your thoughts and feelings
and relationship with ED.

_____

_____

_____

_____

_____

_____

_____

_____

_____

_____

_____

_____

_____

_____

_____

BLANK PAGE FOR DRAWING, PASTING, MAPPING, & EXPLORING

DATE_____

MORNING REFLECTION

My affirmation for today:

_____

_____

One step I will take today that allows me to leave my comfort zone and leads me closer to my goal:

_____

_____

_____

_____

EVENING REFLECTION

One thing that I am grateful for today and why I am grateful:

_____

_____

_____

_____

A thing I enjoyed today: _____

_____

_____

A person who inspired me today and why they inspired me:_____

_____

_____

_____

_____

My act of connection to others today:_____

_____

_____

_____

_____

A value I lived by today:_____

_____

_____

_____

An emotion I felt today _____ and what

was my emotion trying to tell me?_____

_____

_____

_____

_____

An act of self-compassion today: _____

_____

_____

_____

_____

Did I leave my comfort zone today and do something to bring me closer to my goal?_____

_____

_____

_____

_____

Which wolf did I feed today? _____

_____

_____

_____

_____

SELF-REFLECTIONS

Use this page to explore your thoughts and feelings
and relationship with ED.

_____

_____

_____

_____

_____

_____

_____

_____

_____

_____

_____

_____

_____

_____

_____

_____

BLANK PAGE FOR DRAWING, PASTING, MAPPING, & EXPLORING

DON'T
HIDE

DATE_____

MORNING REFLECTION

My affirmation for today:

_____

_____

One step I will take today that allows me to leave my comfort zone and leads me closer to my goal:

_____

_____

_____

_____

EVENING REFLECTION

One thing that I am grateful for today and why I am grateful:

_____

_____

_____

_____

A thing I enjoyed today: _____

_____

_____

A person who inspired me today and why they inspired me:_____

_____

_____

_____

_____

My act of connection to others today:_____

_____

_____

_____

A value I lived by today:_____

_____

_____

_____

An emotion I felt today _____ and what

was my emotion trying to tell me?_____

_____

_____

_____

_____

An act of self-compassion today: _____

_____

_____

_____

_____

Did I leave my comfort zone today and do something to bring me
closer to my goal?_____

_____

_____

_____

_____

Which wolf did I feed today? _____

_____

_____

_____

_____

SELF-REFLECTIONS

Use this page to explore your thoughts and feelings
and relationship with ED.

_____

_____

_____

_____

_____

_____

_____

_____

_____

_____

_____

_____

_____

BLANK PAGE FOR DRAWING, PASTING, MAPPING, & EXPLORING

FIND FREEDOM

DATE_____

MORNING REFLECTION

My affirmation for today:

_____

_____

One step I will take today that allows me to leave my comfort zone and leads me closer to my goal:

_____

_____

_____

_____

EVENING REFLECTION

One thing that I am grateful for today and why I am grateful:

_____

_____

_____

_____

A thing I enjoyed today: _____

_____

_____

A person who inspired me today and why they inspired me:_____

_____

_____

_____

_____

My act of connection to others today:_____

_____

_____

_____

A value I lived by today:_____

_____

_____

_____

An emotion I felt today _____ and what

was my emotion trying to tell me?_____

_____

_____

_____

_____

An act of self-compassion today: _____

_____

_____

_____

_____

Did I leave my comfort zone today and do something to bring me

closer to my goal?_____

_____

_____

_____

_____

Which wolf did I feed today? _____

_____

_____

_____

_____

SELF-REFLECTIONS

Use this page to explore your thoughts and feelings
and relationship with ED.

_____

_____

_____

_____

_____

_____

_____

_____

_____

_____

_____

_____

_____

_____

_____

_____

BLANK PAGE FOR DRAWING, PASTING, MAPPING, & EXPLORING

DATE_____

MORNING REFLECTION

My affirmation for today:

_____

_____

One step I will take today that allows me to leave my comfort zone and leads me closer to my goal:

_____

_____

_____

_____

EVENING REFLECTION

One thing that I am grateful for today and why I am grateful:

_____

_____

_____

_____

A thing I enjoyed today: _____

_____

_____

A person who inspired me today and why they inspired me:_____

_____

_____

_____

_____

My act of connection to others today:_____

_____

_____

_____

_____

A value I lived by today:_____

_____

_____

_____

An emotion I felt today _____ and what

was my emotion trying to tell me?_____

_____

_____

_____

_____

An act of self-compassion today: _____

_____

_____

_____

_____

Did I leave my comfort zone today and do something to bring me

closer to my goal?_____

_____

_____

_____

_____

Which wolf did I feed today? _____

_____

_____

_____

_____

SELF-REFLECTIONS

Use this page to explore your thoughts and feelings
and relationship with ED.

_____

_____

_____

_____

_____

_____

_____

_____

_____

_____

_____

_____

_____

_____

BLANK PAGE FOR DRAWING, PASTING, MAPPING, & EXPLORING

DATE_____

MORNING REFLECTION

My affirmation for today:

_____

_____

One step I will take today that allows me to leave my comfort zone and
leads me closer to my goal:

_____

_____

_____

_____

EVENING REFLECTION

One thing that I am grateful for today and why I am
grateful:

_____

_____

_____

_____

A thing I enjoyed today: _____

_____

_____

A person who inspired me today and why they inspired me:_____

_____

_____

_____

_____

My act of connection to others today:_____

_____

_____

_____

_____

A value I lived by today:_____

_____

_____

_____

An emotion I felt today _____ and what

was my emotion trying to tell me?_____

_____

_____

_____

_____

An act of self-compassion today: _____

_____

_____

_____

_____

Did I leave my comfort zone today and do something to bring me

closer to my goal?_____

_____

_____

_____

_____

Which wolf did I feed today? _____

_____

_____

_____

_____

SELF-REFLECTIONS

Use this page to explore your thoughts and feelings
and relationship with ED.

_____

_____

_____

_____

_____

_____

_____

_____

_____

_____

_____

_____

_____

_____

_____

BLANK PAGE FOR DRAWING, PASTING, MAPPING, & EXPLORING

YOU ARE
IMPORTANT

DATE_____

MORNING REFLECTION

My affirmation for today:

_____

_____

One step I will take today that allows me to leave my comfort zone and leads me closer to my goal:

_____

_____

_____

_____

EVENING REFLECTION

One thing that I am grateful for today and why I am grateful:

_____

_____

_____

_____

A thing I enjoyed today: _____

_____

_____

A person who inspired me today and why they inspired me:_____

_____

_____

_____

_____

My act of connection to others today:_____

_____

_____

_____

A value I lived by today:_____

_____

_____

_____

An emotion I felt today _____ and what

was my emotion trying to tell me?_____

_____

_____

_____

_____

An act of self-compassion today: _____

_____

_____

_____

_____

Did I leave my comfort zone today and do something to bring me

closer to my goal?_____

_____

_____

_____

_____

Which wolf did I feed today? _____

_____

_____

_____

_____

SELF-REFLECTIONS

Use this page to explore your thoughts and feelings
and relationship with ED.

_____

_____

_____

_____

_____

_____

_____

_____

_____

_____

_____

_____

_____

_____

BLANK PAGE FOR DRAWING, PASTING, MAPPING, & EXPLORING

KEEP
GOING

DATE_____

MORNING REFLECTION

My affirmation for today:

_____

_____

One step I will take today that allows me to leave my comfort zone and leads me closer to my goal:

_____

_____

_____

_____

EVENING REFLECTION

One thing that I am grateful for today and why I am grateful:

_____

_____

_____

_____

A thing I enjoyed today: _____

_____

_____

A person who inspired me today and why they inspired me:_____

_____

_____

_____

_____

My act of connection to others today:_____

_____

_____

_____

A value I lived by today:_____

_____

_____

An emotion I felt today _____ and what

was my emotion trying to tell me?_____

_____

_____

_____

_____

An act of self-compassion today: _____

_____

_____

_____

_____

Did I leave my comfort zone today and do something to bring me
closer to my goal?_____

_____

_____

_____

_____

Which wolf did I feed today? _____

_____

_____

_____

_____

SELF-REFLECTIONS

Use this page to explore your thoughts and feelings
and relationship with ED.

_____

_____

_____

_____

_____

_____

_____

_____

_____

_____

_____

_____

_____

_____

_____

BLANK PAGE FOR DRAWING, PASTING, MAPPING, & EXPLORING

YOU ARE
WORTHY OF
HAPPINESS

DATE_____

MORNING REFLECTION

My affirmation for today:

_____

_____

One step I will take today that allows me to leave my comfort zone and leads me closer to my goal:

_____

_____

_____

_____

EVENING REFLECTION

One thing that I am grateful for today and why I am grateful:

_____

_____

_____

_____

A thing I enjoyed today: _____

_____

_____

A person who inspired me today and why they inspired me:_____

_____

_____

_____

_____

My act of connection to others today:_____

_____

_____

_____

A value I lived by today:_____

_____

_____

An emotion I felt today _____ and what

was my emotion trying to tell me?_____

_____

_____

_____

_____

An act of self-compassion today: _____

_____

_____

_____

_____

Did I leave my comfort zone today and do something to bring me closer to my goal?_____

_____

_____

_____

_____

Which wolf did I feed today? _____

_____

_____

_____

_____

SELF-REFLECTIONS

Use this page to explore your thoughts and feelings
and relationship with ED.

_____

_____

_____

_____

_____

_____

_____

_____

_____

_____

_____

_____

_____

_____

_____

_____

BLANK PAGE FOR DRAWING, PASTING, MAPPING, & EXPLORING

you are
magnificent

DATE_____

MORNING REFLECTION

My affirmation for today:

_____

_____

One step I will take today that allows me to leave my comfort zone and leads me closer to my goal:

_____

_____

_____

_____

EVENING REFLECTION

One thing that I am grateful for today and why I am grateful:

_____

_____

_____

_____

A thing I enjoyed today: _____

_____

_____

A person who inspired me today and why they inspired me:_____

_____

_____

_____

_____

My act of connection to others today:_____

_____

_____

_____

_____

A value I lived by today:_____

_____

_____

_____

An emotion I felt today _____ and what

was my emotion trying to tell me?_____

_____

_____

_____

_____

An act of self-compassion today: _____

_____

_____

_____

_____

Did I leave my comfort zone today and do something to bring me closer to my goal?_____

_____

_____

_____

_____

Which wolf did I feed today? _____

_____

_____

_____

_____

SELF-REFLECTIONS

Use this page to explore your thoughts and feelings
and relationship with ED.

_____

_____

_____

_____

_____

_____

_____

_____

_____

_____

_____

_____

_____

BLANK PAGE FOR DRAWING, PASTING, MAPPING, & EXPLORING

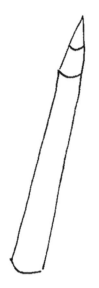

you are a survivor

DATE_____

MORNING REFLECTION

My affirmation for today:

_____

_____

One step I will take today that allows me to leave my comfort zone and leads me closer to my goal:

_____

_____

_____

_____

EVENING REFLECTION

One thing that I am grateful for today and why I am grateful:

_____

_____

_____

_____

A thing I enjoyed today: _____

_____

_____

A person who inspired me today and why they inspired me:_____

_____

_____

_____

_____

My act of connection to others today:_____

_____

_____

_____

_____

A value I lived by today:_____

_____

_____

_____

An emotion I felt today _____ and what

was my emotion trying to tell me?_____

_____

_____

_____

_____

An act of self-compassion today: _____

_____

_____

_____

_____

Did I leave my comfort zone today and do something to bring me closer to my goal?_____

_____

_____

_____

Which wolf did I feed today? _____

_____

_____

_____

_____

SELF-REFLECTIONS

Use this page to explore your thoughts and feelings
and relationship with ED.

_____

_____

_____

_____

_____

_____

_____

_____

_____

_____

_____

_____

_____

_____

BLANK PAGE FOR DRAWING, PASTING, MAPPING, & EXPLORING

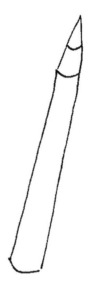

YOU ARE
COMPLETE

DATE_____

MORNING REFLECTION

My affirmation for today:

_____

_____

One step I will take today that allows me to leave my comfort zone and leads me closer to my goal:

_____

_____

_____

_____

EVENING REFLECTION

One thing that I am grateful for today and why I am grateful:

_____

_____

_____

_____

A thing I enjoyed today: _____

_____

_____

A person who inspired me today and why they inspired me:_____

_____

_____

_____

_____

My act of connection to others today:_____

_____

_____

_____

A value I lived by today:_____

_____

_____

_____

An emotion I felt today _____ and what

was my emotion trying to tell me?_____

_____

_____

_____

_____

An act of self-compassion today: _____

_____

_____

_____

_____

Did I leave my comfort zone today and do something to bring me

closer to my goal?_____

_____

_____

_____

_____

Which wolf did I feed today? _____

_____

_____

_____

_____

SELF-REFLECTIONS

Use this page to explore your thoughts and feelings
and relationship with ED.

_____

_____

_____

_____

_____

_____

_____

_____

_____

_____

_____

_____

_____

_____

BLANK PAGE FOR DRAWING, PASTING, MAPPING, & EXPLORING

mistakes allow growth

DATE_____

MORNING REFLECTION

My affirmation for today:

_____

_____

One step I will take today that allows me to leave my comfort zone and leads me closer to my goal:

_____

_____

_____

_____

EVENING REFLECTION

One thing that I am grateful for today and why I am grateful:

_____

_____

_____

_____

A thing I enjoyed today: _____

_____

_____

A person who inspired me today and why they inspired me:_____

_____

_____

_____

_____

My act of connection to others today:_____

_____

_____

_____

_____

A value I lived by today:_____

_____

_____

_____

An emotion I felt today _____ and what

was my emotion trying to tell me?_____

_____

_____

_____

_____

An act of self-compassion today: _____

_____

_____

_____

_____

Did I leave my comfort zone today and do something to bring me

closer to my goal?_____

_____

_____

_____

_____

Which wolf did I feed today? _____

_____

_____

_____

_____

SELF-REFLECTIONS

Use this page to explore your thoughts and feelings
and relationship with ED.

_____

_____

_____

_____

_____

_____

_____

_____

_____

_____

_____

_____

_____

_____

_____

BLANK PAGE FOR DRAWING, PASTING, MAPPING, & EXPLORING

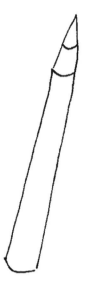

YOU ARE
BRAVE

DATE_____

MORNING REFLECTION

My affirmation for today:

_____

_____

One step I will take today that allows me to leave my comfort zone and leads me closer to my goal:

_____

_____

_____

_____

EVENING REFLECTION

One thing that I am grateful for today and why I am grateful:

_____

_____

_____

_____

A thing I enjoyed today: _____

_____

_____

A person who inspired me today and why they inspired me:_____

_____

_____

_____

_____

My act of connection to others today:_____

_____

_____

_____

A value I lived by today:_____

_____

_____

_____

An emotion I felt today _____ and what

was my emotion trying to tell me?_____

_____

_____

_____

_____

An act of self-compassion today: _____

_____

_____

_____

_____

Did I leave my comfort zone today and do something to bring me closer to my goal?_____

_____

_____

_____

Which wolf did I feed today? _____

_____

_____

_____

_____

SELF-REFLECTIONS

Use this page to explore your thoughts and feelings
and relationship with ED.

_____

_____

_____

_____

_____

_____

_____

_____

_____

_____

_____

_____

_____

_____

_____

_____

BLANK PAGE FOR DRAWING, PASTING, MAPPING, & EXPLORING

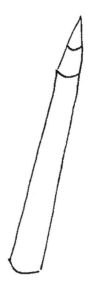

YOU ARE
GENUINELY
LOVED

DATE_____

MORNING REFLECTION

My affirmation for today:

_____

_____

One step I will take today that allows me to leave my comfort zone and leads me closer to my goal:

_____

_____

_____

_____

EVENING REFLECTION

One thing that I am grateful for today and why I am grateful:

_____

_____

_____

_____

A thing I enjoyed today: _____

_____

_____

A person who inspired me today and why they inspired me:_____

_____

_____

_____

_____

My act of connection to others today:_____

_____

_____

_____

A value I lived by today:_____

_____

_____

An emotion I felt today _____ and what

was my emotion trying to tell me?_____

_____

_____

_____

_____

An act of self-compassion today: _____

_____

_____

_____

_____

Did I leave my comfort zone today and do something to bring me closer to my goal?_____

_____

_____

_____

Which wolf did I feed today? _____

_____

_____

_____

_____

SELF-REFLECTIONS

Use this page to explore your thoughts and feelings
and relationship with ED.

_____

_____

_____

_____

_____

_____

_____

_____

_____

_____

_____

_____

_____

_____

_____

BLANK PAGE FOR DRAWING, PASTING, MAPPING, & EXPLORING

its ok to rest

DATE_____

MORNING REFLECTION

My affirmation for today:

_____

_____

One step I will take today that allows me to leave my comfort zone and leads me closer to my goal:

_____

_____

_____

_____

EVENING REFLECTION

One thing that I am grateful for today and why I am grateful:

_____

_____

_____

_____

A thing I enjoyed today: _____

_____

_____

A person who inspired me today and why they inspired me:_____

_____

_____

_____

_____

My act of connection to others today:_____

_____

_____

_____

A value I lived by today:_____

_____

_____

An emotion I felt today _____ and what

was my emotion trying to tell me?_____

_____

_____

_____

_____

An act of self-compassion today: _____

_____

_____

_____

_____

Did I leave my comfort zone today and do something to bring me closer to my goal?_____

_____

_____

_____

_____

Which wolf did I feed today? _____

_____

_____

_____

_____

SELF-REFLECTIONS

Use this page to explore your thoughts and feelings
and relationship with ED.

_____

_____

_____

_____

_____

_____

_____

_____

_____

_____

_____

_____

_____

_____

BLANK PAGE FOR DRAWING, PASTING, MAPPING, & EXPLORING

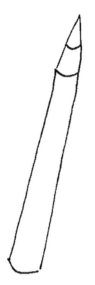

keep going
fantastic
person

DATE_____

MORNING REFLECTION

My affirmation for today:

_____

_____

One step I will take today that allows me to leave my comfort zone and leads me closer to my goal:

_____

_____

_____

_____

EVENING REFLECTION

One thing that I am grateful for today and why I am grateful:

_____

_____

_____

_____

A thing I enjoyed today: _____

_____

_____

A person who inspired me today and why they inspired me:_____

_____

_____

_____

_____

My act of connection to others today:_____

_____

_____

_____

_____

A value I lived by today:_____

_____

_____

_____

An emotion I felt today _____ and what

was my emotion trying to tell me?_____

_____

_____

_____

_____

An act of self-compassion today: _____

_____

_____

_____

_____

Did I leave my comfort zone today and do something to bring me closer to my goal?_____

_____

_____

_____

_____

Which wolf did I feed today? _____

_____

_____

_____

_____

SELF-REFLECTIONS

Use this page to explore your thoughts and feelings
and relationship with ED.

_____

_____

_____

_____

_____

_____

_____

_____

_____

_____

_____

_____

_____

_____

_____

BLANK PAGE FOR DRAWING, PASTING, MAPPING, & EXPLORING

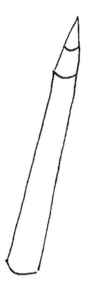

be a rainbow

DATE_____

MORNING REFLECTION

My affirmation for today:

_____

_____

One step I will take today that allows me to leave my comfort zone and leads me closer to my goal:

_____

_____

_____

_____

EVENING REFLECTION

One thing that I am grateful for today and why I am grateful:

_____

_____

_____

_____

A thing I enjoyed today: _____

_____

_____

A person who inspired me today and why they inspired me:_____

_____

_____

_____

_____

My act of connection to others today:_____

_____

_____

_____

_____

A value I lived by today:_____

_____

_____

_____

An emotion I felt today _____ and what

was my emotion trying to tell me?_____

_____

_____

_____

_____

An act of self-compassion today: _____

_____

_____

_____

_____

Did I leave my comfort zone today and do something to bring me closer to my goal?_____

_____

_____

_____

_____

Which wolf did I feed today? _____

_____

_____

_____

_____

SELF-REFLECTIONS

Use this page to explore your thoughts and feelings
and relationship with ED.

_____

_____

_____

_____

_____

_____

_____

_____

_____

_____

_____

_____

_____

_____

BLANK PAGE FOR DRAWING, PASTING,
MAPPING, & EXPLORING

YOU ARE
BEAUTIFUL

DATE_____

MORNING REFLECTION

My affirmation for today:

_____

_____

One step I will take today that allows me to leave my comfort zone and leads me closer to my goal:

_____

_____

_____

_____

EVENING REFLECTION

One thing that I am grateful for today and why I am grateful:

_____

_____

_____

_____

A thing I enjoyed today: _____

_____

_____

A person who inspired me today and why they inspired me:_____

_____

_____

_____

_____

My act of connection to others today:_____

_____

_____

_____

_____

A value I lived by today:_____

_____

_____

_____

An emotion I felt today _____ and what

was my emotion trying to tell me?_____

_____

_____

_____

_____

An act of self-compassion today: _____

_____

_____

_____

_____

Did I leave my comfort zone today and do something to bring me closer to my goal?_____

_____

_____

_____

_____

Which wolf did I feed today? _____

_____

_____

_____

_____

SELF-REFLECTIONS

Use this page to explore your thoughts and feelings
and relationship with ED.

_____

_____

_____

_____

_____

_____

_____

_____

_____

_____

_____

_____

_____

_____

_____

_____

BLANK PAGE FOR DRAWING, PASTING, MAPPING, & EXPLORING

change is
beautiful

DATE_____

MORNING REFLECTION

My affirmation for today:

_____

_____

One step I will take today that allows me to leave my comfort zone and leads me closer to my goal:

_____

_____

_____

_____

EVENING REFLECTION

One thing that I am grateful for today and why I am grateful:

_____

_____

_____

_____

A thing I enjoyed today: _____

_____

_____

A person who inspired me today and why they inspired me:_____

_____

_____

_____

_____

My act of connection to others today:_____

_____

_____

_____

_____

A value I lived by today:_____

_____

_____

_____

An emotion I felt today _____ and what

was my emotion trying to tell me?_____

_____

_____

_____

_____

An act of self-compassion today: _____

_____

_____

_____

_____

Did I leave my comfort zone today and do something to bring me

closer to my goal?_____

_____

_____

_____

_____

Which wolf did I feed today? _____

_____

_____

_____

_____

SELF-REFLECTIONS

Use this page to explore your thoughts and feelings
and relationship with ED.

_____

_____

_____

_____

_____

_____

_____

_____

_____

_____

_____

_____

_____

_____

_____

_____

BLANK PAGE FOR DRAWING, PASTING, MAPPING, & EXPLORING

you are courageous

DATE_____

MORNING REFLECTION

My affirmation for today:

_____

_____

One step I will take today that allows me to leave my comfort zone and leads me closer to my goal:

_____

_____

_____

_____

EVENING REFLECTION

One thing that I am grateful for today and why I am grateful:

_____

_____

_____

_____

A thing I enjoyed today: _____

_____

_____

A person who inspired me today and why they inspired me:_____

_____

_____

_____

_____

My act of connection to others today:_____

_____

_____

_____

_____

A value I lived by today:_____

_____

_____

_____

An emotion I felt today _____ and what

was my emotion trying to tell me?_____

_____

_____

_____

_____

An act of self-compassion today: _____

_____

_____

_____

_____

Did I leave my comfort zone today and do something to bring me closer to my goal?_____

_____

_____

_____

_____

Which wolf did I feed today? _____

_____

_____

_____

_____

SELF-REFLECTIONS

Use this page to explore your thoughts and feelings
and relationship with ED.

_____

_____

_____

_____

_____

_____

_____

_____

_____

_____

_____

_____

_____

_____

_____

_____

_____

BLANK PAGE FOR DRAWING, PASTING, MAPPING, & EXPLORING

YOU ARE UNIQUE

DATE_____

MORNING REFLECTION

My affirmation for today:

_____

_____

One step I will take today that allows me to leave my comfort zone and leads me closer to my goal:

_____

_____

_____

_____

EVENING REFLECTION

One thing that I am grateful for today and why I am grateful:

_____

_____

_____

_____

A thing I enjoyed today: _____

_____

_____

A person who inspired me today and why they inspired me:_____

_____

_____

_____

_____

My act of connection to others today:_____

_____

_____

_____

A value I lived by today:_____

_____

_____

_____

An emotion I felt today _____ and what

was my emotion trying to tell me?_____

_____

_____

_____

_____

An act of self-compassion today: _____

_____

_____

_____

_____

Did I leave my comfort zone today and do something to bring me closer to my goal?_____

_____

_____

_____

_____

Which wolf did I feed today? _____

_____

_____

_____

_____

SELF-REFLECTIONS

Use this page to explore your thoughts and feelings
and relationship with ED.

_____

_____

_____

_____

_____

_____

_____

_____

_____

_____

_____

_____

_____

_____

_____

BLANK PAGE FOR DRAWING, PASTING, MAPPING, & EXPLORING

DATE_____

MORNING REFLECTION

My affirmation for today:

_____

_____

One step I will take today that allows me to leave my comfort zone and leads me closer to my goal:

_____

_____

_____

_____

EVENING REFLECTION

One thing that I am grateful for today and why I am grateful:

_____

_____

_____

_____

A thing I enjoyed today: _____

_____

_____

A person who inspired me today and why they inspired me:_____

_____

_____

_____

_____

My act of connection to others today:_____

_____

_____

_____

_____

A value I lived by today:_____

_____

_____

_____

An emotion I felt today _____ and what

was my emotion trying to tell me?_____

_____

_____

_____

_____

An act of self-compassion today: _____

_____

_____

_____

_____

Did I leave my comfort zone today and do something to bring me closer to my goal?_____

_____

_____

_____

Which wolf did I feed today? _____

_____

_____

_____

_____

SELF-REFLECTIONS

Use this page to explore your thoughts and feelings
and relationship with ED.

_____

_____

_____

_____

_____

_____

_____

_____

_____

_____

_____

_____

_____

_____

BLANK PAGE FOR DRAWING, PASTING, MAPPING, & EXPLORING

I AM FREE TO CREATE MYSELF

DATE_____

MORNING REFLECTION

My affirmation for today:

_____

_____

One step I will take today that allows me to leave my comfort zone and leads me closer to my goal:

_____

_____

_____

_____

EVENING REFLECTION

One thing that I am grateful for today and why I am grateful:

_____

_____

_____

_____

A thing I enjoyed today: _____

_____

_____

A person who inspired me today and why they inspired me:_____

_____

_____

_____

_____

My act of connection to others today:_____

_____

_____

_____

A value I lived by today:_____

_____

_____

_____

An emotion I felt today _____ and what

was my emotion trying to tell me?_____

_____

_____

_____

_____

An act of self-compassion today: _____

_____

_____

_____

_____

Did I leave my comfort zone today and do something to bring me closer to my goal?_____

_____

_____

_____

_____

Which wolf did I feed today? _____

_____

_____

_____

_____

SELF-REFLECTIONS

Use this page to explore your thoughts and feelings
and relationship with ED.

_____

_____

_____

_____

_____

_____

_____

_____

_____

_____

_____

_____

_____

_____

_____

_____

BLANK PAGE FOR DRAWING, PASTING, MAPPING, & EXPLORING

keep being brave

DATE_____

MORNING REFLECTION

My affirmation for today:

_____

_____

One step I will take today that allows me to leave my comfort zone and leads me closer to my goal:

_____

_____

_____

_____

EVENING REFLECTION

One thing that I am grateful for today and why I am grateful:

_____

_____

_____

_____

A thing I enjoyed today: _____

_____

_____

A person who inspired me today and why they inspired me:_____

_____

_____

_____

_____

My act of connection to others today:_____

_____

_____

_____

A value I lived by today:_____

_____

_____

_____

An emotion I felt today _____ and what

was my emotion trying to tell me?_____

_____

_____

_____

_____

An act of self-compassion today: _____

_____

_____

_____

_____

Did I leave my comfort zone today and do something to bring me closer to my goal?_____

_____

_____

_____

_____

Which wolf did I feed today? _____

_____

_____

_____

_____

SELF-REFLECTIONS

Use this page to explore your thoughts and feelings
and relationship with ED.

_____

_____

_____

_____

_____

_____

_____

_____

_____

_____

_____

_____

_____

_____

_____

BLANK PAGE FOR DRAWING, PASTING, MAPPING, & EXPLORING

YOU ARE
STRONG

APPENDIX A – VALUES

Acceptance
Accomplishment
Achievement
Altruism
Ambition
Assertiveness
Bravery
Calmness
Commitment
Community
Compassion
Competence
Confidence
Connection
Consistency
Contentment
Control
Cooperation
Courage
Creativity
Curiosity
Decisiveness
Dedication
Dependability
Determination
Discovery
Empathy
Endurance
Enthusiasm
Equality
Excellence
Expressiveness
Fairness

Faith
Fame
Fearlessness
Fidelity
Freedom
Friendship
Generosity
Gratitude
Greatness
Growth
Happiness
Honesty
Hope
Humility
Imaginative
Independence
Individuality
Inquisitiveness
Inspirational
Integrity
Intelligence
Intuitiveness
Joyfulness
Justice
Kindness
Knowledge
Logical
Love
Loyalty
Mastery
Motivation
Openness
Optimism

Originality
Patience
Peace
Persistence
Playfulness
Power
Productivity
Reason
Recognition
Recreation
Reflective
Respect
Responsibility
Self-reliance
Selflessness
Serenity
Sincerity
Skillfulness
Solitude
Spirituality
Spontaneity
Strength
Thoughtfulness
Tolerance
Tranquillity
Transparency
Trust
Understanding
Visionary
Vitality
Wealth
Wisdom

APPENDIX B – EMOTIONS

APPENDIX C – AFFIRMATIONS

SAMPLE AFFIRMATIONS

MY OWN AFFIRMATIONS

I am complete just as I am

I am capable of anything I put my mind to

I am resilient

I am lovable

I am loving and kind

I am worthy

I am valuable

I am secure

I am unique

I am beautiful just as I am

I am talented

I am amazing

I am inspirational

I am calm and caring

I am courageous

I am the creator of my life

I am full of humor

I am surrounded by friends

I am genuine and giving

I am happy

I am positive energy

I am a powerful

I am indestructible

I am strong

I am determined

I am at peace with my surroundings

I am grateful for my life as it is

I deserve all good things that come my way

This book has been created by Maria Ganci, Psychotherapist and Clinical Social Worker, and Dr. Linsey Atkins, Clinical Psychologist. It is dedicated to all adolescents who have been afflicted by an eating disorder.

Each of the hundreds of teenagers and young adults we have worked with has inspired us and shown boundless creativity, intelligence, and potential. It is unfortunate that these brilliant adolescents have been imprisoned by an eating disorder that challenges their enormous gifts and potential. It is only through guiding and encouraging these young people to rediscover, believe, and accept their true worth that recovery is possible. We hope this journal can relieve them of some of their suffering and provide support through their difficult journey toward recovery.

Their recovery is a great gift to us.

We would also like to express our sincere thanks to Hayley Edwards, who has contributed her wonderful artwork to many of the journal pages, and also Sara, whose invaluable comments have been much appreciated.

MARIA & LINSEY

APT THERAPEUTIC SOLUTIONS

www.apttherapeuticsolutions.com

Made in the USA
Middletown, DE
13 February 2022